TRAVEL
CHECKLIST
JOURNAL

A PORTABLE TRIP PLANNER AND DIARY

BY CLAUDINE GANDOLFI

PETER PAUPER PRESS, INC.
WHITE PLAINS, NEW YORK

PETER PAUPER PRESS
Fine Books and Gifts Since 1928

Our Company

In 1928, at the age of twenty-two, Peter Beilenson began printing books on a small press in the basement of his parents' home in Larchmont, New York. Peter—and later, his wife, Edna—sought to create fine books that sold at "prices even a pauper could afford."

Today, still family owned and operated, Peter Pauper Press continues to honor our founders' legacy—and our customers' expectations—of beauty, quality, and value.

Designed by Margaret Rubiano
Images used under license from Shutterstock.com

Printed in China

7 6 5 4

Visit us at www.peterpauper.com

THIS TRAVEL JOURNAL BELONGS TO:

....

CONTACT INFORMATION:

....

....

....

TABLE OF CONTENTS

INTRODUCTION

Need a break? You've earned it! Are you envisioning yourself on a luxurious hammock in the Caribbean, cool drink in hand, as you while away the sun-soaked hours doing absolutely nothing? Or is seeing the dazzling sights of Paris, while shopping on the Champs-Élysées, more your style? Do you see yourself hiking through the highlands of Scotland, surfing Manly Beach near Sydney, or cruising to Alaska? Whatever you choose, we invite you to use this portable planner and trip journal to help you actualize your dream vacation or holiday.

Use the undated calendar to visualize your plans and help you see where you'll have extra time and where you won't. Where will you visit? When? Has someone recommended a hotel, apartment, or hostel, or are you going to do your own research? We can help you figure all that out. Make sure to leave enough time for travel between home and your home away from home. Are there "must visit" attractions or restaurants where you're going? Keep a list of where you'd like to go but leave time for rest and for soaking up local color.

Pack your bags with our helpful packing checklist. It's easier to pack less, though that may seem counterintuitive. You'll have room for a new scarf, sweater, or souvenir if you don't overpack. Plan to pack clothing that coordinates so you can swap and reuse items. Remember adapters and power cords!

This portable volume will help you plan it all and then record your memories once you're there. It's the perfect keepsake of your trip. *Bon voyage!*

VITALS

PERSONAL INFO

Passport Number ....

Driver's License Number ....

Known Traveler Number (KTN)/TSA PreCheck...

....

Lost/Stolen Card Hotlines ....

....

....

....

Miscellaneous ....

....

....

....

....

....

....

....

....

MEDICAL INFO

PHYSICIAN ....

Telephone ....

Conditions ....

....

....

....

....

Prescriptions/Dosage ....

....

....

....

....

....

....

....

CONTACTS

NAME ....

Address ....

....

Phone Number ....

Email ....

———•———

NAME ....

Address ....

....

Phone Number ....

Email ....

———•———

NAME ....

Address ....

....

Phone Number ....

Email ....

PRE-TRIP CHECKLIST

- [ ] Hold newspaper, mail, or other deliveries
- [ ] Arrange for boarding of pets, or hire a pet-sitter. Keep the number handy when you travel.
- [ ] If traveling by car, arrange to have pre-trip servicing. Your mechanic should check fluids, tires, tire pressure, and other important things.
- [ ] Check passports—they should be current for six months or more.
- [ ] Check for visa regulations in the countries to which you're traveling.
- [ ] Check for any immunization requirements, and follow up with your doctor.
- [ ] Sign up for Global Entry (it includes TSA PreCheck and an interview is needed) or Clear (if you want to speed through all the security lines).
- [ ] If you don't have Global Entry and are a U.S. citizen traveling internationally, you should also consider Mobile Passport (https://mobilepassport.us/) to make going through U.S. Customs a breeze.
- [ ] Join the S.T.E.P. (https://step.state.gov/) program for any travel warnings if traveling internationally.
- [ ] Ensure that you have sufficient prescription medicine for the duration of your trip, plus extra just in case.
- [ ] Check the weather at your destination.
- [ ] Purchase trip cancellation and additional medical insurance, if needed.
- [ ] Make copies of travel documents.
- [ ] Get all necessary gear for your electronics.
- [ ] Research entrance fees for museums and other sites.
- [ ] If traveling internationally, inform credit and debit card companies of plans. Line up the most economical mobile calling plan.
- [ ] Research trip destinations. Watch travel videos, read guidebooks, and visit online sites.
- [ ] Check on host country tipping and service policies.
- [ ] Make note of any public or religious holidays for destinations to check for closings of museums and other sites, or changes in public transportation schedules.
- [ ] Confirm all reservations one week ahead and make any special requests (i.e., early check-in) at that time.

PLANNING TIPS

ONE-MONTH CALENDAR

Write in all your trip details, including dates, times, and locations of arrivals and

SU	M	T	W

departures; lodging names and dates; and restaurant or excursion plans.

TH	F	S	NOTES

PACKING LIST

BASICS

- [ ] Reading material
- [ ] Gum and snacks
- [ ] Ear plugs
- [ ] Phone/tablet
- [ ] Travel pillow
- [ ] Headphones
- [ ] Credit and debit cards
- [ ] Foreign currency (if needed)
- [ ] Passport/visa
- [ ] Driver's license
- [ ] Tickets/Itinerary
- [ ] Confirmation of reservations
- [ ] Travel guide book/maps
- [ ] Water bottle
- [ ] Pen and note pad
- [ ] Hand sanitizer
- [ ] Disinfecting wipes
- [ ] Day bag
- [ ] Jewelry

CLOTHES

- [ ] Underwear
- [ ] Socks
- [ ] Undershirts/bras
- [ ] Pantyhose
- [ ] Pajamas/bathrobe
- [ ] Slippers
- [ ] Shirts
- [ ] T-shirts
- [ ] Pants/shorts
- [ ] Jeans
- [ ] Skirts/dresses
- [ ] Suits
- [ ] Shoes/boots
- [ ] Sneakers
- [ ] Flip-flops/sandals
- [ ] Raincoat
- [ ] Jacket
- [ ] Sweaters
- [ ] Bathing suit/cover-up
- [ ] Exercise clothes

TOILETRIES

- [ ] Shampoo/conditioner
- [ ] Soap
- [ ] Other hair products
- [ ] Toothbrush/toothpaste
- [ ] Mouthwash
- [ ] Dental floss
- [ ] Deodorant
- [ ] Moisturizer
- [ ] Makeup/makeup remover
- [ ] Comb/brush
- [ ] Hair dryer
- [ ] Razor/shaving cream
- [ ] Cotton swabs
- [ ] Tweezers
- [ ] Mirror
- [ ] Nail file
- [ ] Nail polish/remover
- [ ] Feminine hygiene items
- [ ] Eyeglasses/contact lenses
- [ ] Cleaning products for contact lenses

ADDITIONAL ITEMS

- [ ] Insect repellent
- [ ] Sunscreen
- [ ] Hat
- [ ] Chargers
- [ ] Sunglasses
- [ ] Medications
- [ ] Umbrella
- [ ] Emergency contacts
- [ ] Binoculars
- [ ] Headlamp or mini flashlight
- [ ] OTC medicine for travel-related issues
- [ ] Dryer sheets—to keep luggage smelling fresh
- [ ] Packing cubes
- [ ] ....
- [ ] ....
- [ ] ....
- [ ] ....
- [ ] ....

DON'T FORGET

THINGS I STILL NEED TO DO

SAFETY TIPS/BUDGET

- Keep a copy of important information, such as passport number, flight info, and destination address(es), on a separate sheet of paper. Print out several, and keep a copy in your luggage, your carry-on, and leave one at home.

- Pack a change of clothes and phone charger in your carry-on in case of a lost luggage disaster.

- Always pack your medication in your carry-on bag. Make copies of your prescriptions. Keep one copy in your carry-on and another copy inside your checked luggage.

- Pack a handful of zip-lock bags in various sizes for storing wet items, toiletries, small souvenirs, etc. They take up almost no space and have dozens of uses. A pillowcase makes a handy laundry bag.

- Keep a cosmetic case or pouch filled with travel sizes of shampoo, lotion, and other toiletries. When you're ready, you can just pick up and go, rather than hunt down individual items.

- A small battery-powered reading light can be a lifesaver. Your cellphone also makes a handy flashlight in an emergency. It will provide sufficient light to find your car keys or unlock a door.

- Try to plan your travel to a new city for arrival during daylight hours. This may not always be possible, but it will allow you to control some of the safety issues.

- Look for airport shuttles and taxis that will take you directly to where you are staying. Uber may be a good choice too. Stay away from local taxis waiting just outside the airport or bus station.

- If you travel during the off-season, you can save money and avoid throngs of people. You can find better rates on flights, accommodations, entertainment, and more by going to your destination during a less popular time.

- Traveling on the weekends is the most expensive. If you can get a flight during the middle of the week, you can save some real money that can come in handy later.

- Save on your food budget by packing food. If you rent a house or apartment, you could buy groceries to make your own meals, and you're less reliant on eating out.

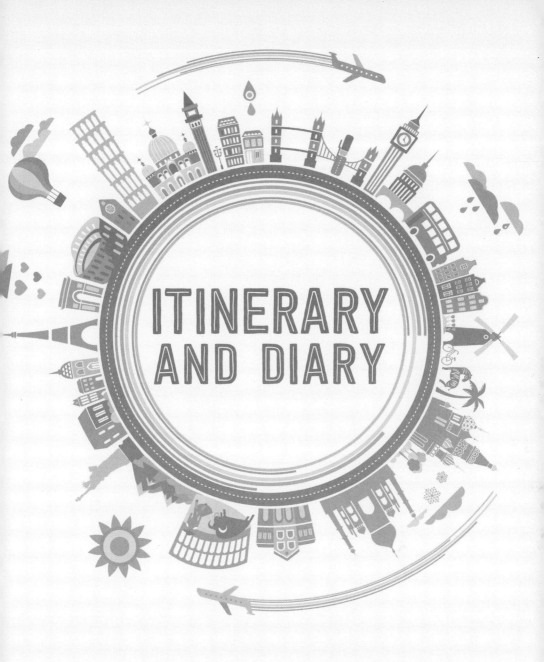

ITINERARY AND DIARY

This section provides four pages of guided prompts for each day of your trip, to record memorable details, impressions, and highlights.

DAY 1

DATE .... **Weather**

Destination/location ....

....

....

How to get there ....

....

....

Travel companions ....

....

Activities ....

....

....

Hotel ....

....

Restaurants ....

....

....

Entertainment ....

....

BEST PART OF TODAY

DAY 1

FUN STORY FROM TODAY

WHAT I'LL REMEMBER MOST

IF I EVER RETURN, I NEED TO

WHAT I DIDN'T LIKE

DATE .... **Weather**

Destination/location ....

....

....

How to get there ....

....

....

Travel companions ....

....

Activities ....

....

....

Hotel ....

....

Restaurants ....

....

....

Entertainment ....

....

BEST PART OF TODAY

DAY 2

FUN STORY FROM TODAY

WHAT I'LL REMEMBER MOST

IF I EVER RETURN, I NEED TO

WHAT I DIDN'T LIKE

DAY 3

DATE .... **Weather**

Destination/location ....
....
....

How to get there ....
....
....

Travel companions ....
....

Activities ....
....
....

Hotel ....
....

Restaurants ....
....
....

Entertainment ....
....

BEST PART OF TODAY

DAY 3

FUN STORY FROM TODAY

_____

_____

_____

_____

_____

_____

_____

_____

WHAT I'LL REMEMBER MOST

_____

_____

_____

_____

_____

_____

_____

_____

IF I EVER RETURN, I NEED TO

WHAT I DIDN'T LIKE

DAY 4

DATE .... **Weather** ☁ ☀ ☁ 🌧

Destination/location ....
....
....

How to get there ....
....
....

Travel companions ....
....

Activities ....
....
....

Hotel ....
....

Restaurants ....
....
....

Entertainment ....
....

BEST PART OF TODAY

DAY 4

FUN STORY FROM TODAY

WHAT I'LL REMEMBER MOST

IF I EVER RETURN, I NEED TO

WHAT I DIDN'T LIKE

DAY 5

DATE .... **Weather**

Destination/location ....

....

....

How to get there ....

....

....

Travel companions ....

....

Activities ....

....

....

Hotel ....

....

Restaurants ....

....

....

Entertainment ....

....

BEST PART OF TODAY

DAY 5

FUN STORY FROM TODAY ....

....

....

....

....

....

....

....

....

....

....

WHAT I'LL REMEMBER MOST ....

....

....

....

....

....

....

....

....

....

....

IF I EVER RETURN, I NEED TO

WHAT I DIDN'T LIKE

DAY 6

DATE .... **Weather**

Destination/location ....
....
....

How to get there ....
....
....

Travel companions ....
....

Activities ....
....
....

Hotel ....
....

Restaurants ....
....
....

Entertainment ....
....

BEST PART OF TODAY

DAY 6

FUN STORY FROM TODAY

WHAT I'LL REMEMBER MOST

IF I EVER RETURN, I NEED TO

WHAT I DIDN'T LIKE

DAY 7

DATE .... **Weather**

Destination/location ....
....
....

How to get there ....
....
....

Travel companions ....
....

Activities ....
....
....

Hotel ....
....

Restaurants ....
....
....

Entertainment ....
....

BEST PART OF TODAY

DAY 7

FUN STORY FROM TODAY

WHAT I'LL REMEMBER MOST

IF I EVER RETURN, I NEED TO

WHAT I DIDN'T LIKE

DAY 8

DATE .... **Weather**

Destination/location ....

....

....

How to get there ....

....

....

Travel companions ....

....

Activities ....

....

....

Hotel ....

....

Restaurants ....

....

....

Entertainment ....

....

BEST PART OF TODAY

DAY 8

FUN STORY FROM TODAY

WHAT I'LL REMEMBER MOST

IF I EVER RETURN, I NEED TO

WHAT I DIDN'T LIKE

DAY 9

DATE .... **Weather**

Destination/location ....
....
....

How to get there ....
....
....

Travel companions ....
....

Activities ....
....
....

Hotel ....
....

Restaurants ....
....
....

Entertainment ....
....

BEST PART OF TODAY

DAY 9

FUN STORY FROM TODAY

WHAT I'LL REMEMBER MOST

IF I EVER RETURN, I NEED TO

WHAT I DIDN'T LIKE

DAY 10

DATE .... **Weather**

Destination/location ....
....
....

How to get there ....
....
....

Travel companions ....
....

Activities ....
....
....

Hotel ....
....

Restaurants ....
....
....

Entertainment ....
....

BEST PART OF TODAY

DAY 10

FUN STORY FROM TODAY

WHAT I'LL REMEMBER MOST

IF I EVER RETURN, I NEED TO

WHAT I DIDN'T LIKE

DAY 11

DATE .... **Weather**

Destination/location ....
....
....

How to get there ....
....
....

Travel companions ....
....

Activities ....
....
....

Hotel ....
....

Restaurants ....
....
....

Entertainment ....
....

BEST PART OF TODAY

DAY 11

FUN STORY FROM TODAY

WHAT I'LL REMEMBER MOST

IF I EVER RETURN, I NEED TO

WHAT I DIDN'T LIKE

DAY 12

DATE .... **Weather**

Destination/location ....

....

....

How to get there ....

....

....

Travel companions ....

....

Activities ....

....

....

Hotel ....

....

Restaurants ....

....

....

Entertainment ....

....

BEST PART OF TODAY

DAY 12

FUN STORY FROM TODAY

WHAT I'LL REMEMBER MOST

IF I EVER RETURN, I NEED TO

WHAT I DIDN'T LIKE

DAY 13

DATE .... **Weather**

Destination/location ....
....
....

How to get there ....
....
....

Travel companions ....
....

Activities ....
....
....

Hotel ....
....

Restaurants ....
....
....

Entertainment ....
....

BEST PART OF TODAY

DAY 13

FUN STORY FROM TODAY

WHAT I'LL REMEMBER MOST

IF I EVER RETURN, I NEED TO

WHAT I DIDN'T LIKE

DAY 14

DATE .... **Weather**

Destination/location ....

....

....

How to get there ....

....

....

Travel companions ....

....

Activities ....

....

....

Hotel ....

....

Restaurants ....

....

....

Entertainment ....

....

....

BEST PART OF TODAY

DAY 14

FUN STORY FROM TODAY

WHAT I'LL REMEMBER MOST

IF I EVER RETURN, I NEED TO

WHAT I DIDN'T LIKE

REFLECTIONS

FAVORITE SIGHTS

....

....

....

....

....

....

FAVORITE ACTIVITIES

....

....

....

....

....

....

WHO I MET

....

....

....

....

FAVORITE RESTAURANTS OR FOODS

....

....

....

....

NOTABLE SHOPPING

....

....

....

....

REFLECTIONS

DETOURS/UNEXPECTED ADVENTURES

WHAT TO REMEMBER FOR NEXT TIME

NOTES

FOREIGN PHRASES

ENGLISH	FRENCH	SOUNDS LIKE
Hello	Bonjour	(bohn-zhoor)
Good evening	Bon soir	(bohn swah)
Please	S'il vous plaît	(sill voo pleh)
Where is the bathroom?	Où sont les toilettes?	(Ooo son lays twah-lehts?)
I'm sorry, I don't speak French	Je suis désolé, je ne parle pas Français	(zhuh swee day-zoh-lay, zhuh nuh parl pah frahn-say)
How much does that cost?	Ça coûte combien?	(Sah koot kombee-en?)
Thank you	Merci	(mare-see)
Good-bye	Au revoir	(oh-vwar)

ENGLISH	SPANISH	SOUNDS LIKE
Hello	Hola	(oh-lah)
Please	Por favor	(por-fa-bor)
Where is the bathroom?	¿Dónde están los servicios?	(dohn-day ay-stahn lohs sehr-bee-thee-ohs)
I'm sorry, I don't speak Spanish	Lo siento, no hablo español	(loh-see-ehn-toh no ah-bloh ay-spahn-yohl)
How much does that cost?	¿Cuánto cuesta?	(kwahn-toh kway-stah)
Thank you	Gracias	(grah-thee-ahs)
Good-bye	Adios	(ah-dee-ohs)

ENGLISH	ITALIAN	SOUNDS LIKE
Hi/Bye	Ciao	(chow)
Good morning	Buon giorno	(boo-ohn jeeor-no)
Good afternoon/ evening	Buona sera	(boo-ohna sehr-ah)
Good night	Buona notte	(boo-ohna noh-tay)
Please	Per favore	(pair fah-voh-reh)
Where is the bathroom?	Dov'è il bagno?	(Doh-veh eel bah-nyoh)
I'm sorry, I don't speak Italian	Mi dispiace, non parlo italiano	(mee dees-pya-che, non par-lo ay-tal-lee-on-o)
How much is this?	Quanto costa?	(kwan-toh cost-ah)
Thank you	Grazie	(grah-tsee-ay)
Good-bye	Arrivederci	(ah-ree-veh-dehr-chee)

METRIC CONVERSIONS

DISTANCE

1 inch (in) = 2.54 centimeters (cm)

1 yard (yd) = 0.91 meters (m)

3.28 feet (ft) = 1 meter (m)

1 mile (mi) = 1.61 kilometers (km)

0.62 mile (mi) = 1 kilometer (km)

VOLUME

1 ounce (oz) = 29.57 milliliters (ml)

8 ounces (oz) = 236.59 milliliters (ml)

33.81 fluid ounces (oz) or .26 gallons = 1 liter

WEIGHT

1 ounce (oz) = 28.35 grams (g)

1 pound = 0.45 kilograms (kg)

2.20 pounds = 1 kilogram (kg)

AREA

1 hectare = 10,000 m^2 = 2.47 acres

TEMPERATURE

32 degrees Fahrenheit (°F) = 0 degrees Celsius (°C)

50 degrees Fahrenheit (°F) = 10 degrees Celsius (°C)

68 degrees Fahrenheit (°F) = 20 degrees Celsius (°C)

86 degrees Fahrenheit (°F) = 30 degrees Celsius (°C)